Big Thoughts for Little Thinkers
By Daniel Thompson

Illustrated by Connor Edwards

CCM BOOKS

First Published by Carefully Crafted Media in 2020

Copyright ©Daniel Thompson 2020

ISBN: 978-1-9998295-4-4

For my Mom and Dad.

A Few Thoughts on:

Happiness 6

Progress 8

Other People 9

Making Mistakes 10

Success 13

Worry 14

Doing your Chores 15

Fussy Eaters 16

Self Improvement 17

The Importance of Trying 18

Making Plans 19

Countries 21

Being Different 22

Gods 23

Self Love 24

Being You 26

Love 27

Manners 28

Being Perfect 30

The Joys of Being a Human Doing 32

Happiness

Nowadays it seems to me,
That happiness is sought,
Amongst the miles of shopping aisles,
Of things we haven't bought.

And it certainly seems suggested,
That should we wish to smile,
We need to buy this something new,
And add it to our pile.

But I believe that something new,
With happiness attached,
May make us happy for a while,
But rarely does it last.

'Til off we dash, with wads of cash,
To find another store.
Searching shelves for something else,
Forever needing more.

A new TV, a fancy bike,
An old antique you thought you'd like.
You buy and buy all day and night,
And though you try it's never right.

Tomorrow brings another this,
More happiness you're told you'll miss.
No matter how your pile grows,
Your happy heart just comes and goes.

But maybe! What if? Just hear me out...
Things are not what life's about.
And maybe even, I'd suggest,
They'll never bring you happiness.

Perhaps that feeling that you crave,
Is not in every purchase made.
But from instead the simple things,
That lift you up and give you wings.

Like laughing 'til your sides are sore,
Amongst the people you adore.
Perhaps you'll find the happy part,
Was always there inside your heart.

Perhaps you'll see without a doubt,
Things are things, you can live without.
And once that's clear, perhaps you'll see,
You're as happy as you choose to be.

Progress

Always be slightly too deep for your feet,
And never intending to stay.
For it's a real shame,
When extraordinary brains,
Are used in an ordinary way.

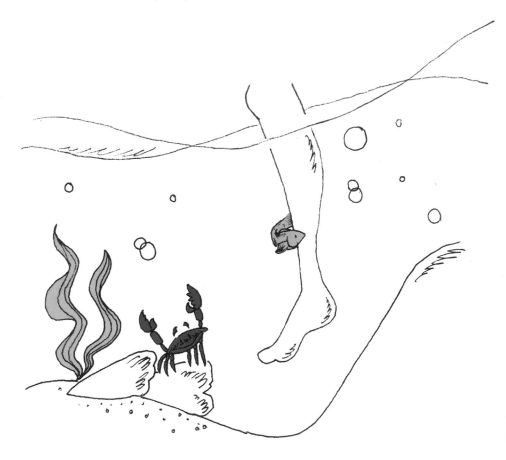

Other People

Some people have dimples,
Or freckles, or pimples,
Big noses, small ears or no teeth.

But it's not who you are,
On the surface that counts,
It's the person who lives underneath.

Making Mistakes

Everybody makes mistakes,
That much I can confirm.
You can view them as a problem,
Or instead, a chance to learn.

For every great success that comes,
Is built upon the rubble,
Of accidents and failed attempts,
And countless hours of trouble.

But what you take from each mistake,
Remains inside your brain.
So when you start things over,
You won't make that one again.

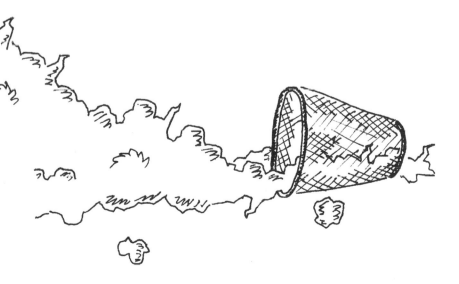

Success

Why is it in dreams,
A successful life means,
Money, big houses and stuff?
And is the intention,
To fail to mention,
How much of this stuff is enough?

I mean, when you're old,
Will the memories you hold,
Be the mountains of stuff that you own?
Or the moments in love,
And the things that you've done,
And the wonderful people you've known?

No, I'd say you're successful,
If life isn't stressful,
If calm finds a home in your head.
If you earn enough money,
For food in your tummy,
And a reason to get out of bed.

Any more after that,
You don't need, it's a trap,
You'll just work, and you'll work, till you drop.
So don't! Life is quick,
Only fill it with bits,
Where your heart is so happy it pops.

Look up, find your thing.
Do you dance? Do you sing?
Play a sport? Like to read? Love to nap?
Well I would suggest,
That your life's a success,
If you spend your days doing just that.

Worry

Think of worries,
Inside your head,
As useless bags,
Of rocks instead.

They may be yours,
But have no doubt.
They'll weigh you down,
And wear you out.

So let them go!
Leave them behind!
It's odd at first,
But soon you'll find.

The less you carry,
The less you weigh.
The more you're free,
To enjoy your day.

Doing your Chores

It's perfectly easy,
To feel a bit queasy,
When all of the world's on your mind.

When you open your doors,
To a million chores,
And you feel like you're always behind.

But the best thing to do,
If it happens to you,
Is to put all those chores in a line.

Don't panic, don't stress,
Just take a deep breath,
And knock them off one at a time.

Fussy Eaters

You're not a fussy eater,
You're an eater who's learnt to fuss.
If you question that assumption,
Then this poem is a must.

Suppose you lived not in your house,
Not even in your town.
But deep inside the jungle,
With no super stores around.

Suppose it's been three days or so,
Since you last had your tea.
Do you think, your nose would turn up,
Quite so easily?

Suppose you were an Inuit,
And all you ate was fish.
With fingerfuls of vegetables,
To accompany your dish.

Do you think you'd be so quick,
To push that food away?
Not knowing if you'd get,
Another meal to eat that day?

So next time you have sprouts or peas,
Or Coke instead of Sprite.
Be grateful you have so much choice,
There's food that you don't like.

Self Improvement

If you're wanting to win a gold medal,
Or fly to the moon on a ship.
Or work in a zoo, or be smarter than you,
Take heed of this noteworthy tip.

If ever you think "I can't do that,"
It's important to never forget.
There isn't a something that you cannot do,
Just a something you cannot do yet.

And it sounds a cliché, but just practice each day,
Let the hours turn the weeks into months.
And a moment will come, when that thing will become,
Just a thing that you couldn't do once.

Changes come slow, but just give it a go,
And I'm certain one day if you do.
You'll find in the mirror, a vaguely familiar,
Better, more interesting you.

The Importance of Trying

Life's not a competition,
You don't have to beat the rest.
No, the only thing that matters,
Is you do your very best.

From first to last, to failed or passed,
It matters not a jot.
You can hold your head up,
If you gave it all you've got.

Making Plans

Plans don't always go to plan,
They often change their mind.
Days can go from good to bad,
In barely any time.

Some will call it rotten luck,
And some will call it fate.
But me, I think no matter what,
You have a choice to make.

You can A) be negative,
And get down in the dumps.
Blame yourself for everything,
And moan and groan and grump.

Or you can B) see positives,
Find diamonds in the rough.
Be happy that you did your best,
And know that that's enough.

Your situation stays the same,
That's true, but here's the deal.
The way you choose to look at it,
Will change the way you feel.

19

Countries

The thing about countries,
Of which there are lots.
Is though they seem real,
Well… the truth is they're not.

See, they all face the sun,
And the stars in the sky.
And they all catch the rain,
As the clouds wander by.

And the reason they do,
Shouldn't come as a shock.
As you already know,
Earth's a big ball of rock.

And though there are mountains,
And oceans and reefs.
The same planet Earth,
Can be found underneath.

And once that's agreed,
You will see that perhaps
Our countries are really,
Just lines drawn on maps.

And instead of this fussing,
And fighting for turf.
We could STOP...
And just say,
We all live,
Here,
On EARTH.

Being Different

There's a curious thing about people,
From our toes to our family name.
In some ways we're nothing like anyone else,
And in others, we're all just the same.

We all have a body,
We all have a brain.
One heart, two lungs,
And blood in our veins.

But at the same time you are here on your own,
Your every hair and your every bone,
Is yours and yours only, and it's perfectly true,
You'll never find someone exactly like you.

You're out on your own,
And you're in with the crowd.
You walk your own path,
But you share the same ground.

So don't think of boxes,
Or labels, or names.
No! Nobody's different,
And no-one's the same.

So be open minded,
Give people a shot.
And then just decide,
If you like them or not.

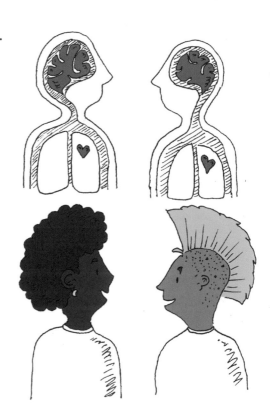

Gods

The truth is no-one's really sure if there's a God or not.
And trust me when I tell you it's been thought about a lot.
But currently there seems to be at least 10,000 versions,
So how should you approach it all? It's hard to know for certain.

But I suggest the thing to do,
Is take some time to think it through.

And ask yourself the question how,
You came to be right here, right now?
And ask yourself the reasons why,
The sun and moon keep passing by?

And ask yourself, then ask once more,
How big is Space and what's it for?
And ask yourself, what's in a cloud?
Ask every question you're allowed.

And let those answers build a floor,
On which you let your brain explore.
And try to find a point of view,
That fits and feels right to you.

But let me say one final thing, whatever you decide,
Your beliefs are yours alone, so keep them safe inside.
Maybe someone's got it right, or maybe, we're all wrong,
But if you are respectful I expect you'll get along.

Self Love

One day your legs will wobble,
When you get up out your chair.
Your skin will spot and wrinkle,
You may even lose your hair!

Your body will be scrumpled,
As you stoop towards the floor.
Your ears, and nose, and eyes and toes,
Won't work quite like before.

And when that's you, you'll stop and look,
At photos on your shelf.
And wonder beyond wonders,
Why you didn't love yourself.

You'll wish above all wishes,
That you could start again.
But not as someone different,
Just as you, inside that frame.

How young you were, how fit you were,
How healthy all your bones once were.
How full of youth and hope you were,
How strong and fit and tall you were.

So next time that your mirror,
Leaves you with a sense of dread.
Stop looking for the bad bits,
And start counting good instead.

You're young, you're tall, your hair is neat,
Your arms are strong, your smile is sweet.
Your eyes are green or brown or blue,
There's lots of things to like on you.

And truth be told, we all have flaws,
So don't waste time hung up on yours.
You're you, you can't be someone else.
So wear your smile, and love yourself.

Being You

Every morning when you wake,
There's two yous you can be.
The second costs a bob or two,
The first's already free.

The second takes all day to do,
The first's already done.
The second has a lot at stake,
The first is rather fun.

The second leads to worry,
Scrutinising what you've said.
The first is freely thinking,
Wondrous thoughts inside your head.

So every morning when you wake,
Which person will you be?
Will you act like someone else?
Or just say I AM ME!

Love

Love is too grand for a sentence,
You can't really put it in words.
But I will tell you this,
From it's very first kiss,
It's not like those stories you've heard.

It isn't the end of a movie,
It isn't a sonnet of prose.
It isn't a ring,
Or some words you can sing,
Or the scent of a sweet smelling rose.

No, love is more like the reaction,
That happens when hearts finally meet.
For some it forms slow,
Others sparkle and glow,
But for every heart it's unique.

So try to forget what I've told you,
Explore love as something brand new.
And I strongly suspect,
That the less you expect,
The more likely you'll find one that's true.

Manners

The curious world of manners,
Is a kind of make pretend.
A list of rules that grown ups use,
With strangers or their friends.

Like always saying thank you.
One should never lick one's knife.
There's at least a baker's dozen,
That you'll learn throughout your life.

And it's nice to act politely,
As should be your expectations.
But it seems a wee bit pompous,
When in certain situations.

In fact I'd be so prudent,
To suggest there is a type.
That hide their somewhat meaner side,
With the fact that they're polite.

That is to say that elbows,
Kept off the dinner table.
May hinge upon the diners,
Of the the well rehearsed and able.

But if those well kept elbows,
Belong upon the arms.
Of somebody who's nasty,
And devoid of any charms.

If they never make you giggle,
Or remotely feel great.
The way some other elbows do,
Whist wondering 'round their plate.

And if those wondering elbows,
On the table all the time.
Are on the arms of someone,
Who is generous and kind.

Well then my friends, I ask you,
With just one plate to give.
Of the two, who would you choose,
To have your dinner with?

So by all means have good manners,
They'll stand you in good stead.
But don't make them your focus,
Make it being kind instead.

For when you're kind to others,
In the things you say and do.
Should you forget good manners,
A good person will shine through.

Being Perfect

Not all bruises find the skin,
No, some are only felt within.

So when you laugh at someone's flaws,
I urge you stop, and think of yours.

Are there things that make you sad?
Or attributes you wish you had?

Now of those things upon your list,
I urge you stop, and think of this.

Do you think you'd be so loud,
If you were stood before a crowd.

Who laughed and jeered with ill intent,
At that which makes you different?

Exactly… you wouldn't like it would you?

So when you see a someone new,
Who's somehow not as great as you.

Think about what we've just said,
And try to find what's good instead.

And where there's weakness, show support,
And build your bridge where theirs fall short.

And use your strengths to help them see,
No-one's perfect. Not you. Not me.

And that's perfectly fine, in fact no, it's better,
'Cause now you can both, be imperfect together.

And friends who accept you the way that you are,
Are the best kind of friends you could hope for by far.

The Joy of Being a Human Doing

When a human being,
Sees a human doing,
A very good deed indeed.
The human doing,
Is without knowing,
Sowing a wonderful seed.

For when good is observed,
Be it seen, or just heard,
A curious moment occurs.
The being that sees it,
Aspires to be it,
And wants to do good in the world.

Now we all have the seeds,
Of some very good deeds,
So plant them wherever you go.
And shower their stalks,
With kind, happy thoughts,
And sun them with love as they grow.

At first it's bare branches,
May garner some glances,
As rushers rush on with their day.
But as it grows higher,
They'll stop to admire,
This beautiful thing in their way.

Then sooner or later,
It's trunk will grow greater,
'Til over the city it towers.
And a wash of grey suits,
Shall stand on its roots,
And behold its magnificent flowers.

Now a life of inspiring,
May sound somewhat tiring,
But the secret that nobody knows.
As you watch your seeds blossom,
Whilst sat on your bottom
A smile forms under your nose.

And it grows… and it grows.. and it grows…

And it didn't cost a dime,
Just seeds and some time,
And a shift of an old point of view.
The secret discovered?
Good deeds towards others,
Will also make you happy too.

With a million pound,
You can still feel down,
But of this I'm most certainly certain.
Happiness manifests,
Not in more, but in less,
And the way you behave as a person.

So instead of just taking,
Take time and try making,
Your planet a happier place.
The more frowns you can turn,
The more happy returns,
To put smiles all over your face.

And if at the start,
Things are slow, don't lose heart,
Stick to the plan and I promise.
Those seeds that you've planted,
Now scruffy and slanted,
Will one day grow up to a forest.

I'm Danny; a poet, film maker, musician and all round creative human from Birmingham.

We live in a world where we often hold ourselves to other people's standards, be it beauty, success, happiness or wealth we tend to look outwardly for confirmation of our achievements and we often forget to question why we do things that way at all.

I wrote this book in hope of illuminating the possibility that perhaps we have what we need to feel successful or beautiful or happy within ourselves already and it is only our perception of those things that we need to change.

I hope you have enjoyed my book and thank you for taking the time to read it.

Keep asking questions.
Keep wondering why.
And remember to always
THINK BIG!

'Big Thought's for Little Thinkers' is Illustrated by Connor Edwards, also from Birmingham. Connor also worked with Danny on 'The Christmas Tale of Elaine Gale' and 'The Humundo Sorterium'.

Check out Danny and Connor's other titles:

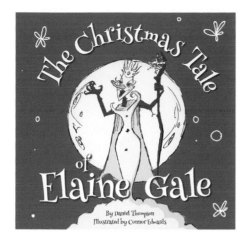

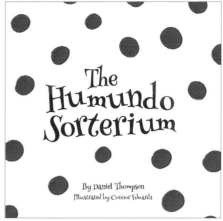

Also check out Danny's ongoing series of
books with Pawprint family:

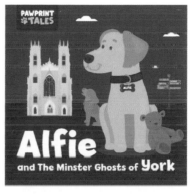

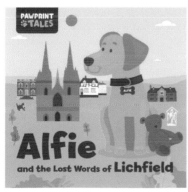

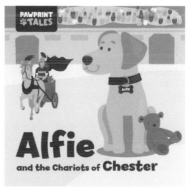

The full selection of titles can be found at:

www.pawprintfamily.com/tales

Printed in Great Britain
by Amazon